200 Essential Sight Words
for Kids Learning to Write and Read

This book belongs to:

_____

Reading & Writing can be fun! Loads of cheerful and interesting illustrations will encourage kids to use this workbook. This 200 essential sight words book helps kids learn to write and read high frequency words in a fun and engaging way.

It is organized in a progressively skill building way for kids to develop confidence to read and write while building vocabulary.

Part 1:
   Practice writing the letters of the alphabet
   Learn to read and write 1 & 2 letter words

Part 2:
   Learn to read and write 3 letter words

Part 3:
   Learn to read and write 4 letter words

Part 4:
   Learn to read and write 5 & 6 letter words

Part 5:
   List of the 200 sight words

This book may require guidance from a teacher, parent or care giver to help the child practice reading & writing.

Meet Jojo.
Jojo is a curious elephant.
He loves to learn and play.
Learn to write & read along with Jojo!

Hi!

My name is Sujatha Lalgudi. I sincerely hope you find my sight words book to be helpful and fun.

Write to me at **sujatha.lalgudi@gmail.com** with the subject: **200 Sight Words** along with **your kid's name** to receive:

- Additional practice worksheets.

- A name tracing worksheet so your kid can practice writing their own name.

- An Award Certificate in Color to gift your child!

If you liked this book, please leave me a review on Amazon! Your kind reviews and comments will encourage me to make more books like this.

Thank you
Sujatha Lalgudi

Part 1:
Learn to read & write
(1 & 2 Letter Sight Words)

- Practice writing the letters of the alphabet
- Trace the sight words and write them on your own
- Trace the sentence with the sight word
- Practice writing the sentence on the blank line
- Mark and color the sight word at the end of the book to show that you have mastered each word!

*Remember: A sentence begins with a capital letter and ends with a period.

Are you ready?
Let's go!

⭐ Celebrate your success! ⭐
Color the star to mark each word you have learnt.

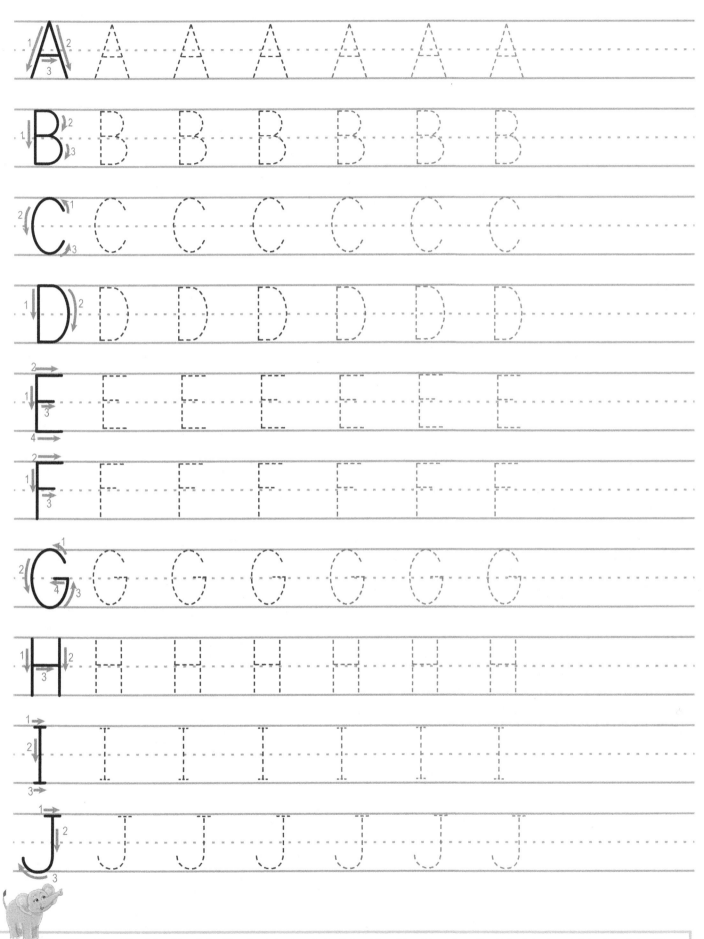

A B C D E F G H I J K L M N O P Q R S T U V W X Y Z

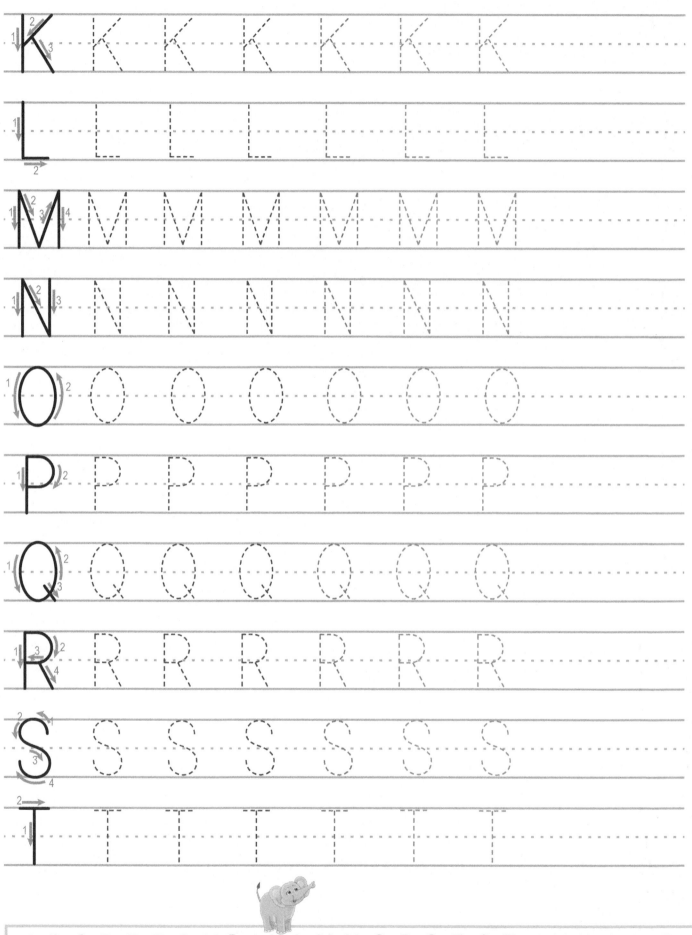

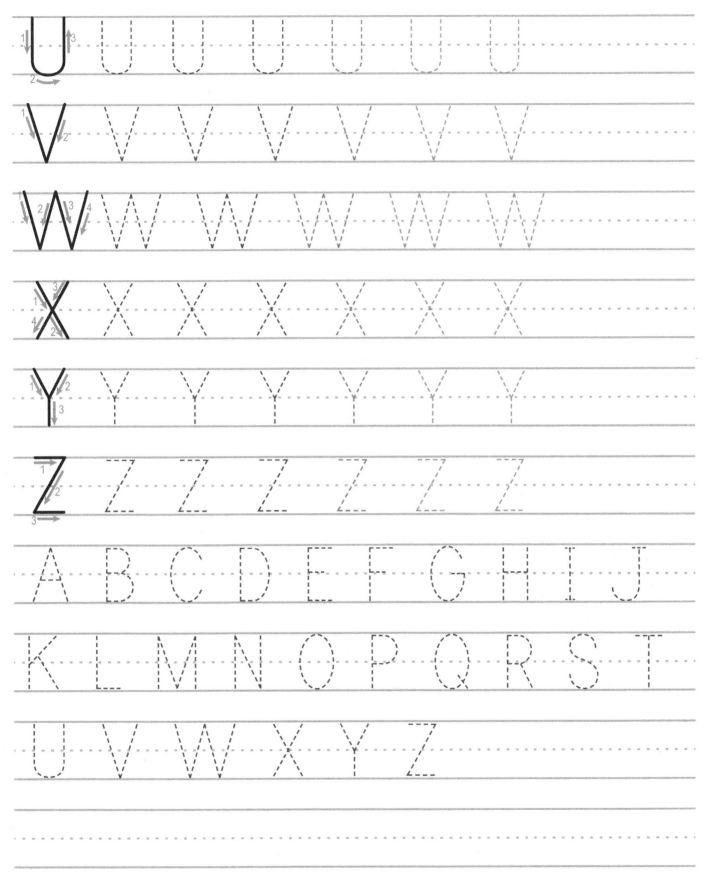

U U U U U U U U U

V V V V V V V V V

W W W W W W W W W

X X X X X X X X X

Y Y Y Y Y Y Y Y Y

Z Z Z Z Z Z Z Z Z

A B C D E F G H I J

K L M N O P Q R S T

U V W X Y Z

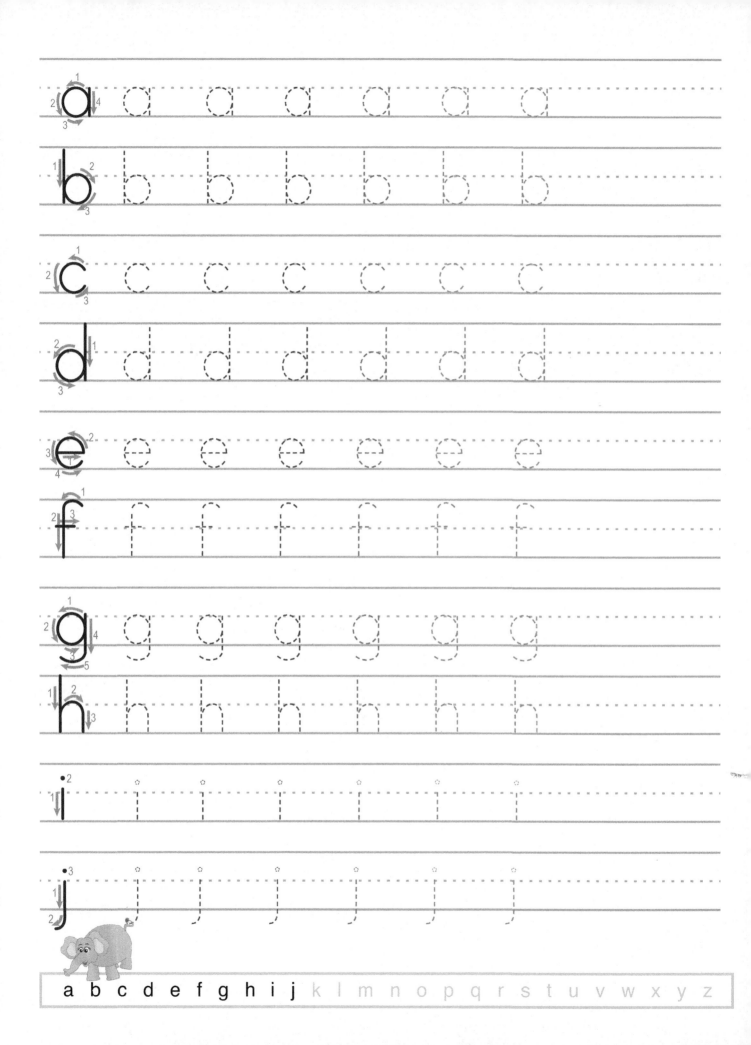

a b c d e f g h i j k l m n o p q r s t u v w x y z

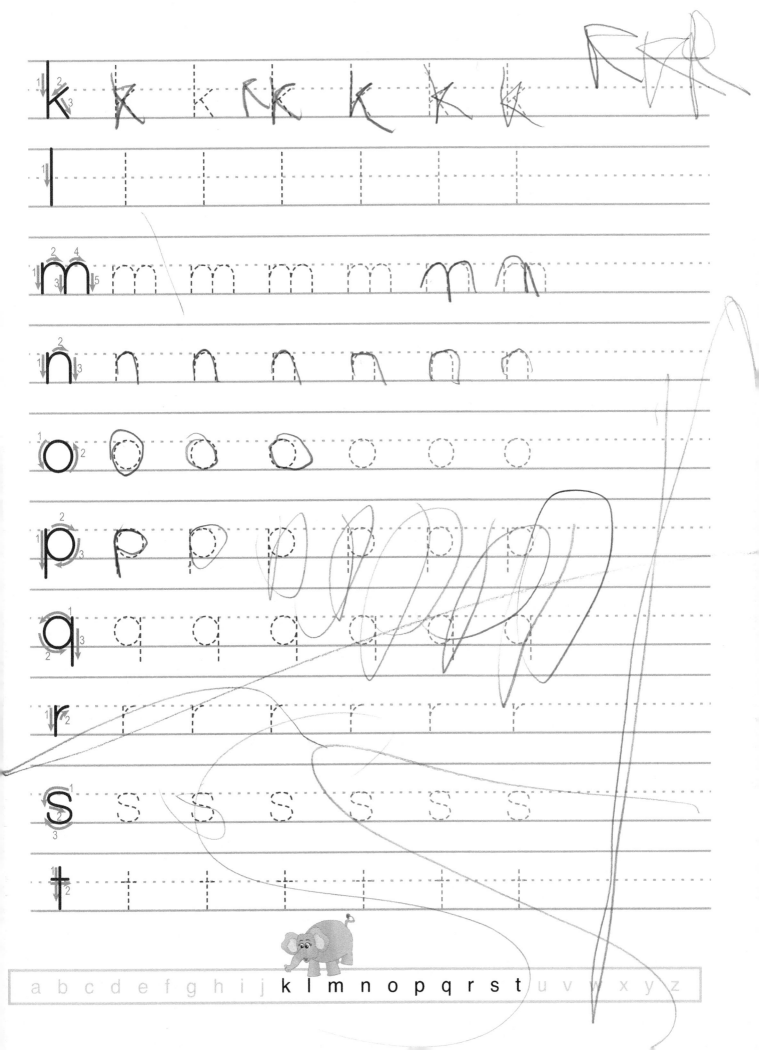

k k k k k k k k

l

m m m m m m m

n n n n n n n n

o o o o o o o

p p p p p p p

q q q q q q

r r r r

s s s s s s

t t t t

a b c d e f g h i j **k l m n o p q r s t** u v w x y z

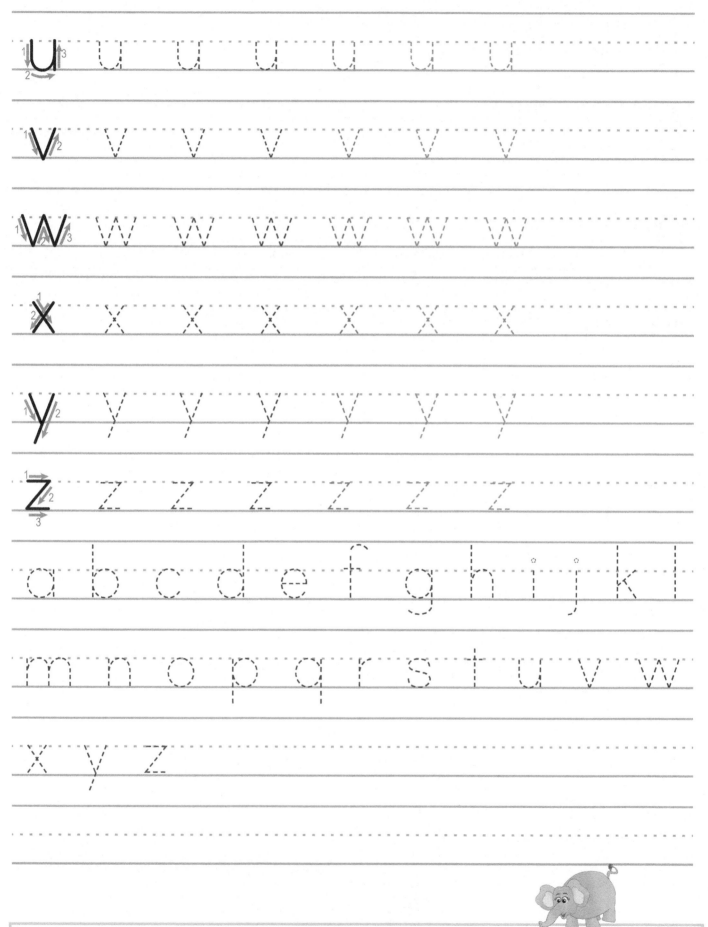

u u u u u u u u

v v v v v v v v

w w w w w w w w

x x x x x x x x

y y y y y y y y

z z z z z z z z

a b c d e f g h i j k l

m n o p q r s t u v w

x y z

a

I have a dog.

a   a   a   a   a   a   a

I have a dog.

★

I

I like my truck.

I   I   I   I   I   I   I

I like my truck.

★

| am | I am five years old. |

am   am   am   am   am

I am five years old.

☆

| an | This is an elephant. |

an   an   an   an   an   an

This is an elephant.

as	I'm busy as a bee.

as   as   as   as   as   as

I'm busy as a bee.

at	Look at the dragon.

at   at   at   at   at   at

Look at the dragon.

be

Could that be Super Boy?

be be be be be

Could that be Super Boy?

by

Sit by the tree.

by by by by by by

Sit by the tree.

do   Do you like this goat?

do do do do do do

Do you like this goat?

☆

go   Can we go on a train?

go go go go go go

Can we go on a train?

☆

he

He is a baby.

he he he he he he

he he he he he he

He is a baby.

He is a baby.

if

Come in if it is cold.

if if if if if if

Come in if it is cold.

in	Put this in the box.

in   in   in   in   in   in

Put this in the box.

is	Her hat is pink.

is   is   is   is   is   is

Her hat is pink.

it	It is a balloon!

it   it   it   it   it   it

It is a balloon!

me	Mom got me a pony.

me   me   me   me   me

Mom got me a pony.

my

This is my room.

my my my my m

This is my room.

☆

no

No jumping on the bed.

no no no no no no

No jumping on the bed.

☆

of

She wore a pair of heels.

of of of of of of of

She wore a pair of heels.

She wore a pair of heels

☆

on

We can go on a plane.

on on on on on on

We can go on a plane.

☆

| or | Do you want tea or milk? |  |

or   or   or   or   or   or

Do you want tea or milk?

Do you want tea or milk?

| so | There are so many coins. |  |

so   so   so   so   so   so

There are so many coins.

to	I like to skate.

to to to to to to

I like to skate.

☆

up	Climb up the ladder.

up up up up up up

Climb up the ladder.

☆

us	The fox can see us.

us   us   us   us   us   us

The fox can see us.

we	We like to snorkel.

we   we   we   we   we

We like to snorkel.

Part 2:

Learn to write & read 3 Letter Sight Words

- Trace the sight words and write them on your own
- Trace the sentence with the sight word
- Practice writing the sentence on the blank line
- Mark and color the sight word at the end of the book to show that you have mastered each word!

You are good at this!

⭐ Celebrate your success! ⭐

Help the bee find the honeycomb and color the picture.

all	He ate all the candy.

all all all all all all

He ate all the candy.

☆

and	Listen and learn.

and and and and and

Listen and learn.

☆

| any | Are there any cows here? |

any   any   any   any   any

Are there any cows here?

| are | These are my toys. |

are   are   are   are   are

These are my toys.

ask   Can you ask him to rake?

ask   ask   ask   ask   ask

Can you ask him to rake?

☆

ate   The dolphin ate the treat.

ate   ate   ate   ate   ate

The dolphin ate the treat.

big

The whale is big.

big big big big big

The whale is big.

☆

but

I am tired, but happy.

but but but but but

I am tired, but happy.

☆

buy | Can we buy icecream?

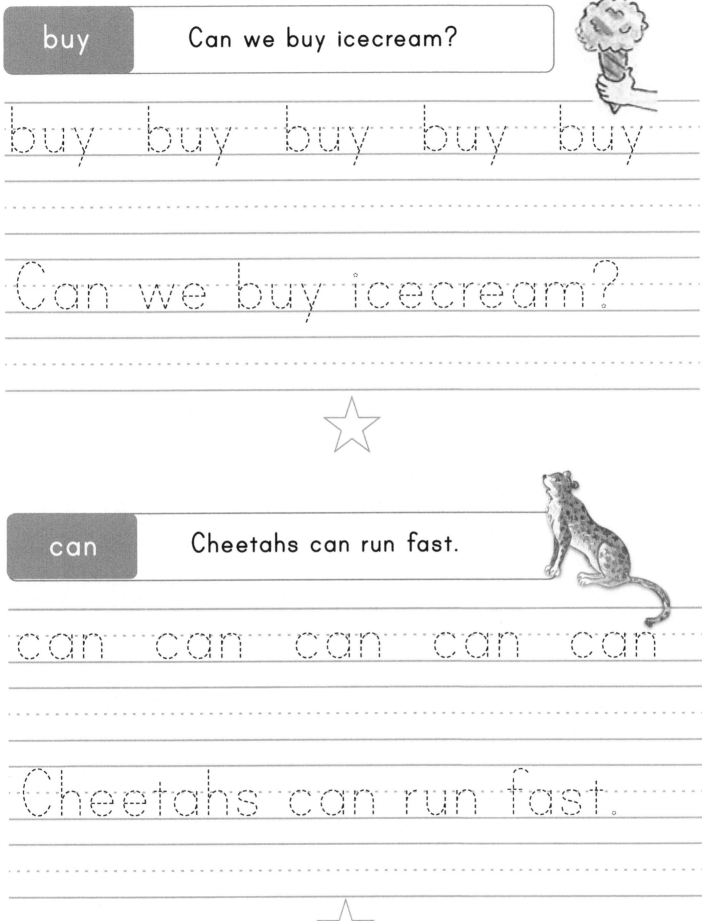

buy buy buy buy buy

Can we buy icecream?

can | Cheetahs can run fast.

can can can can can

Cheetahs can run fast.

day

It is a rainy day.

day day day day day

It is a rainy day.

☆

did

Did you feed the duck?

did did did did did

Did you feed the duck?

☆

eat	Seals eat fish.

eat eat eat eat eat

Seals eat fish.

far	How far can he jump?

far far far far far

How far can he jump?

| fly | Penguins cannot fly. |

fly fly fly fly fly

Penguins cannot fly.

| for | Please look for my sock. |

for for for for for

Please look for my sock.

get	Can you get the ball?	

get   get   get   get   get

Can you get the ball?

got	I got a Christmas gift.

got   got   got   got   got

I got a Christmas gift.

had | The cat had some food.

had had had had had

The cat had some food.

☆

has | The witch has a cauldron.

has has has has has

The witch has a cauldron.

☆

her Look at her castle.

her her her her her

Look at her castle.

Look at

him We like to pet him.

him him him him him

We like to pet him.

| his | He lost his candy cane. |

his his his his his

He lost his candy cane.

| hot | I love hot chocolate. |

hot hot hot hot hot

I love hot chocolate.

how	How does she do that?

how how how how

How does she do that?

☆

let	Let me get a pencil.

let let let let let

Let me get a pencil.

may   May I eat the cake?

may   may   may   may

May I eat the cake?

new   This is my new toy.

new   new   new   new

This is my new toy.

not	Please do not eat that.

not not not not not

Please do not eat that.

now	The ship will sail now.

now now now now

The ship will sail now.

off   The lights went off.

off off off off

The lights went off.

☆

old   My sofa is old.

old old old old

My sofa is old.

☆

one	I have one pet.

one   one   one   one

I have one pet.

our	This is our table.

our   our   our   our

This is our table.

| out | Keep the rabbit out. |

out out out out

Keep the rabbit out.

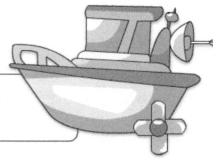

| own | Do you own this boat? |

own own own own

Do you own this boat?

| put | I put away my toys. |

put put put put

I put away my toys.

☆

| ran | The skunk ran away. |

ran ran ran ran

The skunk ran away.

☆

| red | I like red roses. |

red red red red

I like red roses.

| run | My dog likes to run. |

run run run run

My dog likes to run.

| saw | We saw a Toucan. |

saw saw saw saw

We saw a toucan.

| say | Please say yes to the fair. |

say say say say

Please say yes to the fair.

| see | I can see the turkey. |

see see see see

I can see the turkey.

| she | She loves ballet. |

she she she she

She loves ballet.

sit	Please sit down.

sit sit sit sit

Please sit down.

six six six six

Count six turtles.

six	Count six turtles.

| ten | I have ten keys. |

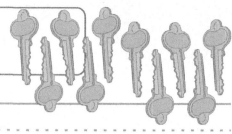

ten   ten   ten   ten

I have ten keys.

| the | My teacher is the best. |

the   the   the   the

My teacher is the best.

| too | I ate too much! |

too too too too

too too to to

I ate too much! *I olt e too*

M u c h

☆

| try | Try on these mittens. |

try try try try

Try on these mittens.

☆

two

These are my two jets.

two   two   two   two   t o

These are my two jets.

use

I use my crayons.

use   use   use   use

I use my crayons.

was	It was time to ski.	

was   was   was   was

It was time to ski.

way	Which way should I go?

way   way   way   way

Which way should I go?

who

Who likes cupcakes?

who who who who

Who likes cupcakes?

why

Why do birds sing?

why why why why

Why do birds sing?

yes	Yes, I have many pets.

yes   yes   yes   yes

Yes, I have many pets.

you	Do you like pizza?

you   you   you   you

Do you like pizza?

Part 3:

Learn to write & read 4 Letter Sight Words

- Trace the sight words and write them on your own
- Trace the sentence with the sight word
- Practice writing the sentence on the blank line
- Mark and color the sight word at the end of the book to show that you have mastered each word!

You are good at this!

⭐ Celebrate your success ⭐
Color these jelly fish!

| away | The parakeet flew away. |  |

away away away

The parakeet flew away.

| been | I have been to the zoo.  |

been been been

I have been to the zoo.

best	He is my best friend.

best best best

He is my best friend.

both	I like both my sisters.

both both both

I like both my sisters.

| came | A clown came home. |

came came came

A clown came home.

| come | Please come inside. |

come come come

Please come inside.

does	Does your hat fit?

does   does   does

Does your hat fit?

done	What have you done?

done   done   done

What have you done?

down | I went down the slide.

down   down   down

I went down the slide.

⭐

find | Find all the Easter eggs.

find   find   find

Find all the Easter eggs.

⭐

| four | A clover has four leaves. |

four four four

A clover has four leaves.

☆

| from | He jumped from the tree. |

from from from

He jumped from the tree.

| gave | I gave him a big hug. |

gave gave gave

I gave him a big hug.

| give | Can you give me candy? |

give give give

Can you give me candy?

This is a good game.

good good good

This is a good game.

☆

Can we grow vegetables?

grow grow grow

Can we grow vegetables?

☆

have

I have a kite.

have have have

I have a kite.

help

I can help you bake.

help help help

I can help you bake.

here   Here is the pie.

here here here

Here is the pie.

hold   Please hold this basket.

hold hold hold

Please hold this basket.

| jump | Can frogs jump? |  |

jump   jump   jump

Can frogs jump?

| just | I just like to sleep early. |

just just just

I just like to sleep early.

keep

Can I keep this toy?

keep keep keep

Can I keep this toy?

⭐

kind

He is kind and helpful.

kind kind kind

He is kind and helpful.

⭐

know	I know how to cook.

know   know   know

I know how to cook.

like   like   like

I like to jump.

like	I like to jump.

long

Giraffes have long necks.

long long long

Giraffes have long necks.

look

Look at this shark.

look look look

Look at this shark.

made   I made these cookies.

made made made

I made these cookies.

☆

many   How many do you see?

many many many

How many do you see?

☆

more   The more the merrier.

more more more

The more the merrier.

☆

much   How much does it cost?

much much much

How much does it cost?

only	I have only one candy.

only only only

I have only one candy.

open	May I open my gift?

open open open

May I open my gift?

part

It is part of the puzzle.

part part part

It is part of the puzzle.

☆

play

I play the violin.

play play play

I play the violin.

☆

pull	Can you pull the wagon?

pull pull pull

Pull push pull. pallx

Can you pull the wagon?

Can you pull the wagon

read	I can read and write.

read read read

I can read and write.

show

I like show and tell.

show   show   show

I like show and tell.

some

Here are some treats.

some   some   some

Here are some treats.

soon   It will be night soon.

soon   soon   soon

It will be night soon.

take   I take the bus to school.

take   take   take

I take the bus to school.

tell

I can tell the time.

tell tell tell

I can tell the time.

that

That dinosaur is huge!

that that that

That dinosaur is huge!

them   Look at them race!

them   them   them

Look at them race!

then   First dinner, then dessert.

then   then   then

First dinner, then dessert.

they	They sleep all day.

they they they

They sleep all day.

☆

this	Is this your umbrella?

this this this

Is this your umbrella?

☆

time	What time is it?

time   time   time

What time is it?

upon	I came upon a snail.

upon   upon   upon

I came upon a snail.

very   The whale is very heavy.

very   very   very

The whale is very heavy.

walk   They walk to school.

walk   walk   walk

They walk to school.

want	I want to meet a unicorn.

want   want   want

I want to meet a unicorn.

warm	It is warm in here.

warm   warm   warm

It is warm in here.

wash   Please wash your hands.

wash wash wash

Please wash your hands.

well   He sings very well.

well well well

He sings very well.

| went | We went up and down. |

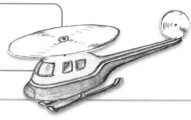

went   went   went

We went up and down.

| were | Fireworks were in the sky. |

were   were   were

Fireworks were in the sky.

what	What do you see?

what what what

What do you see?

when	When can we play?

when when when

When can we play?

will

The sloth will sit still.

will will will

The sloth will sit still.

☆

wish

I wish I could see Santa.

wish wish wish

I wish I could see Santa.

☆

with

I want to play with you.

with   with   with

I want to play with you.

⭐

your

Is this your map?

your   your   your

Is this your map?

⭐

Part 4:

Learn to write & read High Frequency 5 & 6 Letter words
- Trace the sight words and write them on your own
- Trace the sentence with the sight word
- Challenge yourself to write longer sentences
- Mark and color the sight word at the end of the book
  to show that you have mastered each word!

  * The last two are 7 & 8 letter words each

You are amazing!

Celebrate your success!
Color the map!

about Did you learn about space today?

about about about

Did you learn about space today?

after Can we play the piano after this?

after after after

Can we play the piano after this?

again   Try to draw the flower again.

again again again

Try to draw the flower

again.

☆

black   This is a black sea snake.

black

This is a black sea

snake.

☆

bring | Can I bring my gerbil to class?

bring bring bring

Can I bring my gerbil to

class?

☆

brown | These are my new brown shoes.

brown brown brown

These are my new brown

shoes.

☆

carry The truck can carry big loads.

carry carry carry

The truck can carry big loads.

☆

could We could read a book later.

could could could

We could read a book later.

☆

don't   Don't open the oven when baking.

don't don't don't

Don't open the oven
when baking.

☆

drink   Can I drink some apple juice?

drink drink drink

Can I drink some apple
juice?

☆

eight   The octopus has eight limbs.

eight   eight   eight

The octopus has eight

limbs.

every   We like to dance every evening.

every   every   every

We like to dance every

evening.

first | Let us finish our food first.

first first first

Let us finish our food

first.

found | He found my missing sock.

found found found

He found my missing

sock.

funny   My dad is super funny.

funny funny funny

My dad is super funny.

going   We are going on a camping trip.

going going going

We are going on a

camping trip.

green The grass is so green on the hill.

green green green

The grass is so green on
the hill.

laugh I like to laugh
at silly games.

laugh laugh laugh

I like to laugh at silly
games.

light   The sun gives us heat and light.

light   light   light

The sun gives us heat

and light.

never   I have never been to Africa.

never   never   never

I have never been to

Africa.

other   Share the joy with other kids.

other   other   other

Share the joy with other

kids.

right   I like to hop on my right foot.

right   right   right

I like to hop on my right

foot.

round A ball is round and fun to play with.

round round round

A ball is round and fun
to play with.

seven I see seven crabs on the beach.

seven seven seven

I see seven crabs on the
beach.

sleep | Can I sleep after I finish this book?

sleep sleep sleep

Can I sleep after I finish
this book?

small | The mouse is small and fast.

small small small

The mouse is small and
fast.

start	Can we start playing a new game?

start start start

Can we start playing a
new game?

☆

thank	I want to thank everyone for the gifts.

thank thank thank

I want to thank everyone
for the gifts.

☆

their   The eagles soared over their nests.

their their their

The eagles soared over

their nests.

there   My things are there
by the car door.

007

there there there

My things are there by

the car door.

these   Did you wash these green grapes?

these these these

Did you wash these

green grapes?

think   I think you are very smart.

think think think

I think you are very

smart.

those	Those strawberries are delicious.

those those those

Those strawberries are

delicious.

three	I flew three kites this morning.

three three three

I flew three kites this

morning.

today   I saw a beautiful butterfly today.

today today today

I saw a beautiful

butterfly today.

under   My dog is
under the bed.

under under under

My dog is under the

bed.

| water | My fish tank needs more water. |

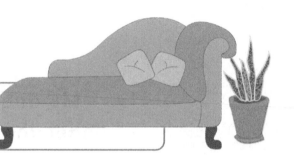

water water water

My fish tank needs more

water.

| where | Where is my potted plant? |

where where where

Where is my potted

plant?

which	Which fruit is your favorite?

which   which   which

Which fruit is your

favorite?

white	Have you seen a white tiger?

white   white   white

Have you seen a white

tiger?

| would | Would you like to paint the fence? |

would   would   would

Would you like to paint
the fence?

⭐

| write | I can read and write very well now. |

write   write   write

I can read and write very
well now.

⭐

always   My dog is always hungry.

always   always

My dog is always hungry.

☆

around   Tie this neatly around the tree.

around   around

Tie this neatly around the

tree.

☆

before | Look before you make that leap.

before before

Look before you make

that leap.

better | I like cake better than candy.

better better

I like cake better than

candy.

| little | I have a naughty little brother. |

little little

I have a naughty little

brother.

| myself | I like to play by myself sometimes. |

myself myself

I like to play by myself

sometimes.

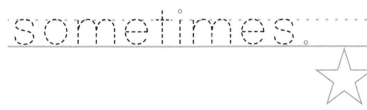

number	I'm very good with numbers.

number number

I'm very good with

numbers.

pretty	My mom is looking very pretty.

pretty pretty

My mom is looking very

pretty.

because

I like painting because
it is a lot of fun.

because because

I like painting because

it is a lot of fun.

together

Together, we can
fix this toy.

together together

Together, we can fix this

toy.

List of Sight Words: 1 to 100

a	I	am	an	as	at	be	by	do	go
he	if	in	is	it	me	my	no	of	on
or	so	to	up	us	we	all	and	any	are
ask	ate	big	but	buy	can	day	did	eat	far
fly	for	get	got	had	has	her	him	his	hot
how	let	may	new	not	now	off	old	one	our
out	own	put	ran	red	run	saw	say	see	she
sit	six	ten	the	too	try	two	use	was	way
who	why	yes	you	away	been	best	both	came	come
does	done	down	find	four	from	gave	give	good	grow

Mark and Color each sight word as and when you complete them!

List of Sight Words: 101 to 200

have	help	here	hold	jump	just	keep	kind	know	like
long	look	made	many	more	much	only	open	part	play
pull	read	show	some	soon	take	tell	that	them	then
they	this	time	upon	very	walk	want	warm	wash	well
went	were	what	when	will	wish	with	your	about	after
again	black	bring	brown	carry	could	don't	drink	eight	every
first	found	funny	going	green	laugh	light	never	other	right
round	seven	sleep	small	start	thank	their	there	these	think
those	three	today	under	water	where	which	white	would	write
always	around	before	better	little	myself	number	pretty	because	together

Mark and Color each sight word as and when you complete them!

200 Sight Words Completed ✓

CONGRATULATIONS!
You are a
CHAMPION!

Recommended next skill

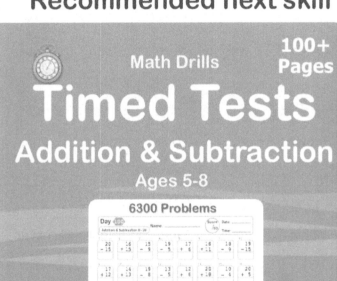

Math Drills

100+ Pages

Timed Tests

Addition & Subtraction

Ages 5-8

6300 Problems

Practice 100 Days of Speed Drills

✓ DAILY PRACTICE ✓ ENHANCE MATH

✓ Get it Today

ISBN: 1679103709

Celebrate your Success!

Share the Joy!

Feel Great Everyday!

Write to me at **sujatha.lalgudi@gmail.com** with the subject:

200 Sight Words along with **your kid's name** to receive:

- Additional practice worksheets.
- A name tracing worksheet so your kid can practice writing their own name.
- An Award Certificate in Color to gift your child!

Congratulations
Writing Super Star
Awarded to

_____

For _____

Date _____   **Signed** _____

Made in the USA
Las Vegas, NV
03 August 2021